M is for monsters:

WHAT IF I KNOW MY ALPHABET

Michelle Nelson-Schmidt

MNS
PRESS

First Edition 2022 | Florida: MNS PRESS, 2022
Text & Illustrations ©Michelle Nelson-Schmidt
All rights reserved. For information contact:
books@MNScreative.com
MNS Press Pensacola, Florida 32506
www.MNScreative.com
Title: M is for Monsters: What if I Know My Alphabet
ISBN Hardback: 978-1-952013-67-6
ISBN Paperback: 978-1-952013-66-9
Printed in the United States of America

F L T X J
K T G X
B K G J
B Y
For my sweet Sage Louise –
may the wonder of letters and words make
your heart sing like they do for your Grandma.
Y
I E Q W

A B C D E F G

A is for APPLE.
B is for BALL.
There are 26 letters,
let's learn them ALL!

O P Q R S T

H I J K L M N

U V W X Y Z

A B C D E F G

C is for CAT.

D is for DOOR.

Read one book and

then read MORE!

O P Q R S T

H I J K L M N

U V W X Y Z

A B C D E F G

E is for ELEPHANT.
F is for FLOWER.
Learning your letters
is a SUPERPOWER!

O P Q R S T

H I J K L M N

U V W X Y Z

A B C D E F G

G is for GOAT.

H is for HAND.

When you sound out a word

it makes you feel GRAND!

O P Q R S T

H I J K L M N

U V W X Y Z

A B C D E F G

I is for ICE CREAM.

J is for JAR.

Words can make stories

that help you go FAR!

O P Q R S T

HIJKLMN

UVWXYZ

A B C D E F G

K is for KITE.
L is for LION.
If this gets hard,
just keep on TRYING!

O P Q R S T

H I J K L M N

U V W X Y Z

A B C D E F G

M is for MONSTER.
N is for NEST.
Keep on going -
do your BEST!

O P Q R S T

HIJKLMN

UVWXYZ

A B C D E F G

O is for OWL.
P is for PEN.
If you mess up,
just try AGAIN!

O P Q R S T

HIJKLMN

UVWXYZ

A B C D E F G

Q is for QUIET.
R is for RABBIT.
Reading books
is a great HABIT!

O P Q R S T

H I J K L M N

U V W X Y Z

A B C D E F G

S is for SUNNY.

T is for TREE.

Ideas and words

set your mind FREE!

O P Q R S T

H I J K L M N

U V W X Y Z

A B C D E F G

U is for UMBRELLA.
V is for VAN.
What if you read?
I know you CAN!

O P Q R S T

H I J K L M N

U V W X Y Z

A B C D E F G

W is for WATCH.
X is for X-RAY.
You're almost there!
Hip, Hip HOORAY!

O P Q R S T

HIJKLMN

UVWXYZ

A B C D E F G

Y is for YARN.

Z is for ZOO.

You're all done!

I'm proud of YOU!

O P Q R S T

HIJKLMN

Petting Zoo

UVWXYZ

What if you know your alphabet?

Aa Bb Cc Dd

Ii Jj Kk Ll

Pp Qq Rr

Vv Ww

Ee Ff Gg Hh

Mm Nn Oo

Ss Tt Uu

Xx Yy Zz

Other titles you might enjoy by Michelle Nelson-Schmidt
Available at www.MNScreative.com

What if I Know My Feelings

What if Know My Opposites

What if I Want to Be Kind

What if I Know My Shapes

Jonathan James and the Whatif Monster

The Whatif Monster Early Reader Chapter Book Series (18 Books)

Herman: A Little Story About Spreading Love

Please, Mind the Bear

Dog and Mouse

Cordelia

Cordelia and the Whale

Bob is a Unicorn

Dogs, Dogs!

Cats, Cats!

Weekly Storytime with Michelle!

Join Michelle every Wednesday at 7:30pm eastern for Storytime Live to hear readings of her books and gift-giveaways! Watch at Facebook.com/MNScreative